# Dan Gets Dressed

Story by Joy Cowley
Illustrations by Annie Hayward

I put on my flying shirt.

2

I put on my flying pants.

3

I put on my flying shoes.

I put on my flying goggles.

I put on my flying gloves.

I put on my zoom-zoom hat.

Now I can fly.
Zoom! Zoom!